Happy Days

stories written by Farrah McDoogle
illustrated by Tom Brannon

Contents

White Plains, New York • Montréal, Québec • Bath, United Kingdom

Our Favorite Animals

"Hey Bert, of all the bugs and animals, what's your favorite?" Ernie wondered one day as the buddies looked around the park.

"Well, I don't know, Ernie," said Bert. "There sure are a lot to choose from—baboons and bears, even spiders, flies, and fleas."

"Don't forget dogs and squirrels...and even the elephants," Ernie reminded him.

"All of those are great," said Bert. "But Bernice is definitely my favorite. None of those is as special as my Bernice, the perfect pigeon."

"You know, Bert, none of those is as special as Rubber Duckie either," Ernie answered. "He will always be my favorite."

4

Play
Song 1

Rubber Duckie

Lyrics and music by Jeff Moss

Rubber Duckie, you're the one.
You make bath time lots of fun.
Rubber Duckie,
I'm awfully fond of you.
Vo-vo dee-o.

Rubber Duckie, joy of joys,
when I squeeze you,
you make noise.
Rubber Duckie,
you're my very best friend,
it's true.

Oh, every day when I
make my way to the tubby,
I find a little fella who's
cute and yellow and chubby.
Rub-a-dub-dubby.

Rubber Duckie, you're so fine
and I'm lucky that you're mine.
Rubber Duckie, I'm
awfully fond of...
Rubber Duckie, I'm
awfully fond of you.

The Animal Fair

I went to the animal fair,
the birds and the beasts
were there.
The big baboon,
by the light of the moon,
was combing his auburn hair.

The monkey bumped the skunk
and sat on the elephant's trunk.
The elephant sneezed
and fell to his knees,
and what became of the monk,
the monk, the monk, the monk,
the monk, the monk, the monk?

Play Song 3

Eency-Weency Spider

Eency-weency spider
went up the waterspout.
Down came the rain
and washed the spider out.

Out came the sun
and dried up all the rain.
The eency-weency spider
went up the spout again.

The Bear Went over the Mountain

The bear went over the
mountain.
The bear went over the
mountain.
The bear went over the
mountain,
to see what he could see,
to see what he could see,
to see what he could see.

The other side of the mountain,
the other side of the mountain,
the other side of the mountain,
was all that he could see,
was all that he could see,
was all that he could see.
The other side of the mountain,
was all that he could see!

Old MacDonald Had a Farm

Old MacDonald had a farm,
E-I-E-I-O.
And on his farm he had a cow,
E-I-E-I-O.
With a *moo, moo* here,
and a *moo, moo* there.
Here a *moo*, there a *moo*,
everywhere a *moo, moo*.
Old MacDonald had a farm,
E-I-E-I-O.

Old MacDonald had a farm,
E-I-E-I-O.
And on his farm he had a pig,
E-I-E-I-O.
With an *oink, oink* here,
and an *oink, oink* there.
Here an *oink*, there an *oink*,
everywhere an *oink, oink*.
Old MacDonald had a farm,
E-I-E-I-O.

Play
Song 6

Five Little Ducks

Five little ducks
went swimming one day,
over the pond and far away.
Mother Duck said,
"Quack, quack, quack, quack."
But only four little ducks
came back.

Four little ducks
went swimming one day,
over the pond and far away.
Mother Duck said,
"Quack, quack, quack, quack."
But only three little ducks
came back.

Three little ducks
went swimming one day,
over the pond and far away.
Mother Duck said,
"Quack, quack, quack, quack."
But only two little ducks
came back.

Two little ducks
went swimming one day,
over the pond and far away.
Mother Duck said,
"Quack, quack, quack, quack."
But only one little
duck came back.

One little duck
went swimming one day,
over the pond and far away.
Mother Duck said,
"Quack, quack, quack, quack."
But none of the five little ducks
came back.

Mother Duck
went swimming one day,
over the pond and far away.
Mother Duck said,
"Quack, quack, quack, quack."
And all of the five little ducks
came back!

Fun with Friends

"Zoe, I really like your pink tutu!" said Abby. "It's sooo enchanting!"

"Ooooh, that made me feel all sunny inside," said Zoe. "I have an idea! Let's all say something nice. I'll go first."

The girls thought that was a great idea.

"Rosita, you dance salsa better than anyone on Sesame Street," Zoe said.

"Ooooh, you're right, Zoe, it feels like sunshine," said Rosita. "*Gracias, amiga.* My turn now! Abby, I love the way you sing. Zoe, your smile makes everybody happy."

"Thanks!" Zoe and Abby giggled together. "*Gracias, amiga*

"I have something to say about all of us!" said Abby. "We're great friends...and that's magical!"

Play Song 1

Sesame Street Theme

Lyrics by Joe Raposo, Bruce Hart, and Jon Stone
Music by Joe Raposo

Sunny day
sweepin' the clouds away,
on my way to
where the air is sweet.
Can you tell me how to get,
how to get to Sesame Street?

Come and play!
Everything's A-OK.
Friendly neighbors there,
that's where we meet.
Can you tell me how to get,
how to get to Sesame Street?

It's a magic carpet ride.
Every door will open wide
to happy people like you.
Happy people like...
What a beautiful...

Sunny day
sweepin' the clouds away,
on my way to
where the air is sweet.
Can you tell me how to get,
how to get to Sesame Street?
How to get to
Sesame Street?

13

If You're Happy and You Know It

If you're happy and you know it,
clap your hands. (Clap twice)
If you're happy and you know it,
clap your hands. (Clap twice)
If you're happy and you know it,
then your face will surely show it!
If you're happy and you know it,
clap your hands. (Clap twice)

If you're happy and you know it,
stomp your feet. (Stomp twice)
If you're happy and you know it,
stomp your feet. (Stomp twice)
If you're happy and you know it,
then your face will surely show it!
If you're happy and you know it,
stomp your feet. (Stomp twice)

Additional verses:
Shout, "Hooray" (Shout, "Hooray")
Do all three (Clap twice, stomp
twice, then shout, "Hooray")

Play
Song 3

Looby Loo

Chorus:
Here we go looby loo.
Here we go looby light.
Here we go looby loo,
all on a Saturday night.

Put your right hand in,
put your right hand out,
then give your right hand a
shake, shake, shake,
and turn yourself about.
(Repeat Chorus)

Additional verses:
Put your left hand in, etc.
Put your right foot in, etc.
Put your left foot in, etc.
Put your whole self in, etc.

A Little Wheel A-Turnin' in My Heart

There's a little wheel
a-turnin' in my heart.
There's a little wheel
a-turnin' in my heart,
in my heart,
in my heart.
There's a little wheel
a-turnin' in my heart.

Oh, I feel so very happy
in my heart.
Oh, I feel so very happy
in my heart.
In my heart,
in my heart;
oh, I feel so very happy
in my heart.

Rig-a-Jig

As I was walking
down the street,
Heigh-o, heigh-o,
heigh-o, heigh-o.

A pretty girl I chanced to meet.
Heigh-o, heigh-o, heigh-o.
Rig-a-jig-jig and away we go,
away we go, away we go.
Rig-a-jig-jig and away we go.
Heigh-o, heigh-o, heigh-o.

Play
Song 6

Polly-Wolly-Doodle

Oh, I went down South
for to see my Sal.
Sing Polly-wolly-doodle all
the day.
My Sally is a spunky gal.
Sing Polly-wolly-doodle all
the day.

Fare thee well,
fare thee well,
fare thee well my fairy fey,
for I'm going to Lou'siana
for to see my Susyanna.
Sing Polly-wolly-doodle all
the day.